Jesus
And The Children

CW00763588

First printing July 2007
16 15 14 13 12 11 10 09 08 07   10 9 8 7 6 5 4 3 2 1

National Library of Australia
Cataloguing-in-Publication entry

    McDonough, Andrew (Andrew John).
    Jesus and the children.
    For primary school children.
    ISBN 9781921229091 (hbk.).
    1. Bible. N.T. Mark X, 13-16 - Juvenile literature. 2.
    Bible stories, English - Juvenile literature. 3. Jesus
    Christ - Juvenile literature. 4. Children in the Bible -
    Juvenile literature. 5. Picture books for children. I.
    Title. (Series : McDonough, Andrew (Andrew John) Lost
    sheep. Series 3 ; 10).
    226.3

Skaterboy stunt double: Samuel Pearce
Behaviour Management Consultant: Pamela McDonough
Comb your hair and tuck your shirt in before reading this book.

Designed and published by Lost Sheep

Lost Sheep
PO Box 3191
Unley SA 5061
Australia
info@lostsheep.com.au
lostsheep.com.au

Printed in China by Color Patch

Jesus
And The Children

Andrew McDonough

It was a busy day for Jesus,
talking to all the grown-ups.

Then along came the mums, hoping Jesus would bless their babies.

"Stop!" said the disciples. "What do you think you're doing? Jesus hasn't got time for babies. Sit over there so you won't get in the way."

Then along came the girls, running towards Jesus.

"Stop!" said the disciples. "What do you think you're doing bothering Jesus? Jesus hasn't got time for girls. Sit down and be quiet while he talks to the grown-ups."

Then one of the boys rolled up to meet Jesus.

"Stop! What do you think you're doing? Jesus hasn't got time for boys and he certainly doesn't approve of skateboards. Sit down and be quiet while Jesus talks to the grown-ups."

But when Jesus saw what the disciples were doing he was . . .

furious!

"What do you think you're doing? Don't stop the children from coming to me!

God's kingdom is for the kids!

Sit down and watch the children, and you will see how to enter the kingdom of God!"

Then the mums brought their babies to Jesus.
And he hugged the babies and blessed them.

Then the girls ran to Jesus. And he hugged the girls and blessed them.

Then one of the boys, who wasn't really into hugging, rolled up. And Jesus blessed him as well because . . .

God's kingdom is for the kids!

The Back Page

Jesus and the Children is based on the story in Mark 10:13–16.
This story shows children how important they are to Jesus and encourages grown-ups to come to him with the simplicity and expectancy of a child.

Before the Story

A good place to start is by asking,
"Do you think Jesus is only interested in the grown-ups?"
"Do you think he is interested in children too?"
Tell them this is a story about Jesus, some children and a bunch of grown-ups.

Read the Story

After the Story

You may like to ask,
"Why do you think the disciples told the children to get out of the way?"
"What did Jesus think about this?"
Have a look back through the pictures together to see when people are sad or cross, but most importantly, when everyone is happy.
Talk about how happy Jesus is when children come to him.

God's blessing,

Andrew